Contents and

This book will introduce the following:

Nouns

A **noun** is a naming word. It can name an **object**.

What **objects** can you see in your room? Say them out loud – they are all **nouns.**

Tick each **noun** below as you find it in the picture.

cat
table ✔
book ✔

bed ✔
lamp ✔
train

bag
picture
box

4

Nouns can also name **people** and **places**.

Draw lines to link these **people** to the **places** where they work.

chef

firefighter

shopkeeper

builder

nurse

shop

hospital

restaurant

building site

fire station

_____

_____

_____

_____

_____

Write down which **places** you have been to this week, such as school or the library. These places are all **nouns.**

Well done!

5

When a **noun** names a particular person it is called a **proper noun** and it begins with a **capital letter**. The **names** of your friends and family are all **proper nouns**.

capital letters

A B C D E F
G H I J K L
M N O P Q
R S T U V
W X Y Z

Write down the **names** of some of your friends.

_____

_____

Make up some funny **names** for these dinosaurs and write them down. Don't forget the **capital letters!**

_____

_____

_____

Days of the week and months of the year are also **proper nouns**.

_____

_____

_____

_____

_____

_____

Write down the **names** of the days of the week using **capital letters** at the beginning.

Fill in the missing months of the year. These **proper nouns** all begin with a **capital letter** too.

months of the year

January	uly
February	ugust
arch	
pril	
	ovember
	ecember

Well done! ⋰

7

When a **noun** names a particular place, like a street, a city or a country, it is also a **proper noun**.

Use the space on the envelope to write your address. Use **capital letters** for your street name, county and country.

Draw circles around the words that are **proper nouns.**

(Europe)   Africa   London

India   river   Antarctica

mountain   Asia   glacier

lake   China   Spain

Capital letters are also used at the beginning of a sentence. A sentence usually ends with a full stop.

Copy the sentences below, but use a capital letter at the beginning of each sentence and for the proper nouns. Don't forget the full stop.

my friends tom and juan live in spain

sarah went to scotland in july

Write a sentence about one of your friends.

Well done!

Plural nouns

Nouns can be singular (one) or plural (more than one). You can turn most **nouns** into **plurals** by adding an **-s** on the end.

 cat

cat**s**

Some **nouns** don't follow this rule:

tomato   ⟶   tomato**es**

child   ⟶   child**ren**

foot   ⟶   f**ee**t

woman   ⟶   wom**e**n

Turn these **single** **nouns** into **plurals.** You might need to change the word, not just add an -s.

tree _____

tooth _____

man _____

hand _____

Collective nouns describe a group of many things.

A **bunch** of flowers
A **flock** of birds
A **fleet** of ships

Some **collective nouns** sound odd!

A **pod** of dolphins
A **pride** of lions
A **trip** of hares
A **litter** of kittens

Make up some silly **collective nouns** for these groups.

_____ of telephones

_____ of insects

_____ of chairs

_____ of pens

_____ of books

Well done!

11

Before a **noun** there is usually an **article**, which tells us whether the object is a general thing or something specific.

'a' or 'an' = **indefinite article**

a house in **an** old street
(one of many)

'the' = **definite article**

the house in **the** old street
(the only one)

Rewrite these sentences so they use the indefinite article 'a'. Use 'an' before a vowel (a, e, i, o, u).

the dog chased the ball

the owl flew into the tree

Nouns that name objects, people and places are sometimes called **concrete nouns** – you can see, touch, taste, smell or hear the object. **Abstract nouns** are feelings and ideas you can't use your senses to identify.

peace

phone

chair

love

Circle all the words you think might be **abstract nouns**. Underline the ones that are **concrete nouns**.

happiness

flower

danger

bravery

computer

ice cream

Well done!

Personal pronouns

If you don't want to repeat a **noun** in a sentence, you can use a **personal pronoun**, to refer to people or objects.

I, me, you, we, us, he, she, it, him, her, they, them

Freddie is hugging **Laura**.
<u>He</u> is hugging <u>her</u>.

| personal pronoun |

I would like you to come and play with me. We can ask Jo too.

Circle the **personal pronouns** in these sentences.

Pick a page of a story book and list all the **personal pronouns** you can find. They appear more often than you think!

14